MIXED NOTICES

NEW POCKET CARTOONS

by

OSBERT LANCASTER

JOHN MURRAY, LONDON, W.1

Osbert Lancaster's other works:

ALL DONE FROM MEMORY (*autobiography*)
PROGRESS AT PELVIS BAY
PILLAR TO POST
HOMES SWEET HOMES
CLASSICAL LANDSCAPE WITH FIGURES
THE SARACEN'S HEAD
DRAYNEFLETE REVEALED
FAÇADES AND FACES
HERE OF ALL PLACES!

Pocket Cartoons:

SIGNS OF THE TIMES 1939–1961
ETUDES '57–'58
LADY LITTLEHAMPTON AND FRIENDS
STUDIES FROM THE LIFE
TABLEAUX VIVANTS
PRIVATE VIEWS
THE YEAR OF THE COMET

Grateful acknowledgement is made to the Editor for kind permission to reprint the following drawings which have appeared in the *Daily Express*

© *Osbert Lancaster* 1963

Printed in Great Britain by Butler & Tanner Ltd., Frome and London, and published by John Murray (Publishers) Ltd., Albemarle Street, London

FOREWORD

The twelve months or so covered by the present volume were a period during which fact, from time to time, outdistanced fiction. There were moments, indeed, particularly during the latter half of the year, when one occasionally wondered whether one was living in Rome during the later Empire, or in France under the Third Republic. Deplorable as such a state of affairs must rightly be judged by those who have the nation's moral welfare professionally at heart, for the cartoonist there were, it must freely be admitted, certain compensations. Censure must, therefore, in his case be tempered by gratitude and it is his sincere hope that the natural remorse now afflicting so many prominent delinquents may be in some degree assuaged by the thought that their conduct, questionable as it may have been, has at least rendered one person's daily task the lighter.

O. L.

"But darling, we can't *all* be stolen!" 22.ix.61

"Am I correct in assuming that membership of
the Common Market will entitle this country to
the free and unrestricted use of the guillotine."
10.x.61

"It's positively uncanny how every major mess our statesmen get us into always turns out in the end to be, morally speaking, *our* fault." 12.x.61

"Make mine a megaton." 18.x.61

"Maud dear, pray explain to me exactly what it is out of which dear Prince Philip is so eager that we should all take our fingers." 19.x.61

"I'm beginning to wonder whether, if any of the nuclear Powers is ever short of a testing site——" 27.x.61

"But that's what one so much admires about Selwyn—once he's made up his mind no power on earth can make him stick to it."

21.xi.61

"I hope you've realised, Miss Flatiron, that if Mr. Heath has his way you'll soon be finding yourself in direct competition with Balenciaga and Chanel." 28.xi.61

"If you ask me it would serve 'em both right
if we handed the Congo straight back to
gallant little Belgium." 1.xii.61

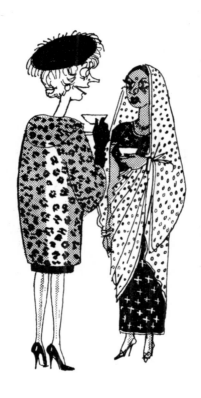

"Of course, dear, one does realise that in view of the grave threat from Goa you naturally want to keep your hands on every bomb you've got." 12.xii.61

"And another thing, Leofric—we should all
be grateful if you would kindly stop referring
to your fellow Magi as the Afro-Asian bloc!"

22.xii.61

"And I should like to take this opportunity of thanking you personally, and all the other Young Conservatives who have put on such a splendid show tonight." 16.i.62

"I'm warning you, Plainsong! The fact that
Fontwater's brought off the All Saints-Holy
Trinity merger won't stop him making a bid
for St. Jude's." 20.i.62

"Sorry if I woke you, Spanielstown, but a rather disturbing thought has just occurred to me. Suppose the world has come to an end!"
6.ii.62

"But why doesn't poor Selwyn do like the rest of us and get himself a really good accountant?" 28.ii.62

"Five—four—three—two—one— LENT!!"

8.iii.62

23

"What a comfort to think, Whortleberry, that all the splendid enthusiasms of our youth are still undimmed—Disarmament, the Reform of the Lords, the Liberal Revival."

15.iii.62

"From I.C.I., Roy Thomson and Charlie
Clore, Good Lord deliver us." 17.iii.62

"Heavens! That reminds me—tomorrow's Mothering Sunday." 31.iii.62

"Withdraw that offer for Berkeley Square
and buy a Renoir—quick!" 10.iv.62

"Tell me, is it true that this M. Pompidou only got his job because his mother was a very close friend of Louis XV?" 17.iv.62

"Of course, without a saliva test one can't
be absolutely sure, but I think I've been
doped!" 19.vi.62

"Fontwater's got a brilliant scheme—suggests
we threaten to put the Abbey up for auction
and thus blackmail the Government into
buying it for the nation!" 1.viii.62

"Ah'll gie you an example of what consti-
tutes 'racial incitement'—makin' dirty cracks
aboot Glasgow Rangers!" 15.viii.62

"'Pon my word, Barnstaple, it must have been worse than the Athenaeum on Boat-race night!" 13.x.62

"We must all hope for all our sakes that the voice which breathed o'er Eden doesn't start breathing o'er the White House." 23.x.62

"Of course, one does see why President Kennedy's just a little nervous—after all, Washington's not *all* that much further from Cuba than London is from Russia." 24.x.62

"Well, dear, the principal difference as far as
I can see is this—a DEfensive weapon is one
with my finger on the trigger, an OFfensive
weapon is one with yours." 26.x.62

"An Underpass, dear child, is the shortest distance between two traffic blocks!" 27.x.62

"You wouldn't by any chance be working in
a highly confidential job at the Admiralty,
would you?" 6.xi.62

"Vassall's replacement seems to be settling
in very satisfactorily." 8.xi.62

"Do you mind telling me, sir, just what it is that makes you think I was bottle-fed?!!"
17.xi.62

"For some of us, m'lady, every year is national productivity year." 23.xi.62

"British scientists, madam, are second to none,
and if only the Government would produce
adequate funds for research we could produce
a weapon that would be just as obsolete as
the Americans' in half the time!" 19.xii.62

22.xii.62

"Well, no one can say the Irish aren't getting
their own back right now!" 3.i.63

"Well, if the power's not off, you might turn on the news and let us hear how our self-indulgence and lack of fibre are wrecking the Gas Board's carefully worked out winter schedule." 24.i.63

"I'm sorry, Jasper, but if staying out of
Europe means we're going to get a little
less of that 'Brecht, Brecht, Brecht,' I'm all
for it!" 1.ii.63

"Tell me, Canon, are you as bored with Pre-marital Intercourse as I am?" 23.ii.63

"Is that the one we swopped for Burgess?"
19.iii.63

"If the Civil Service goes on increasing at the present rate it looks as though the unemployment problem will be solved well before the election!" 20.iii.63

"Restraint! Restraint! It's not one of ours!"
3.iv.63

"O tempora, O mores! Not another djibbah
in sight!" 19.iv.63

"Every now and again I'm overwhelmed by a terrible feeling that life has passed me by— 40 years in the Foreign Service and not a single indecent proposal!" 26.iv.63

"The extraordinary thing is that one never seems to meet any of the remaining two-thirds!" 1.v.63

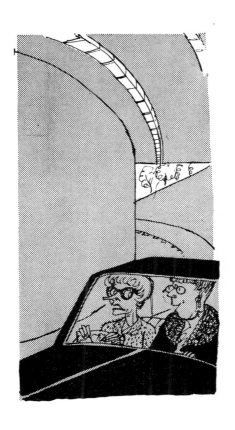

"Tell me, dear, is this the underpass up which Mr. Marples was so warmly recommended to stuff his speech?" 2.v.63

"How odd! I'd half expected to see a strawberry leaf!" 9.v.63

"Jawohl, Herr Kapitan!"
"Aye, aye, Sir!"
"Merde!"

21.v.63

"Old Lotuships is leaving to better himself—
he's just received a very attractive offer from
the Conservative Central Office." 8.vi.63

"I think you must face the fact, Aunt Ethel, that the Cliveden Set has rather changed its character since your day." 11.vi.63

"I do think it's terribly depressing how fickle
the public is—why, now not a single person
has an unkind word to spare for those poor
Argylls!" 12.vi.63

"Darling, I *know* the sun's gone in—it's just
that I can't stand the intolerable brilliance of
Lord Hailsham's halo." 15.vi.63